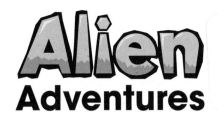

Tin Cat

Tim Little • Jonatronix

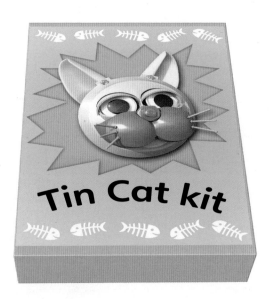

OXFORD

UNIVERSITY PRESS

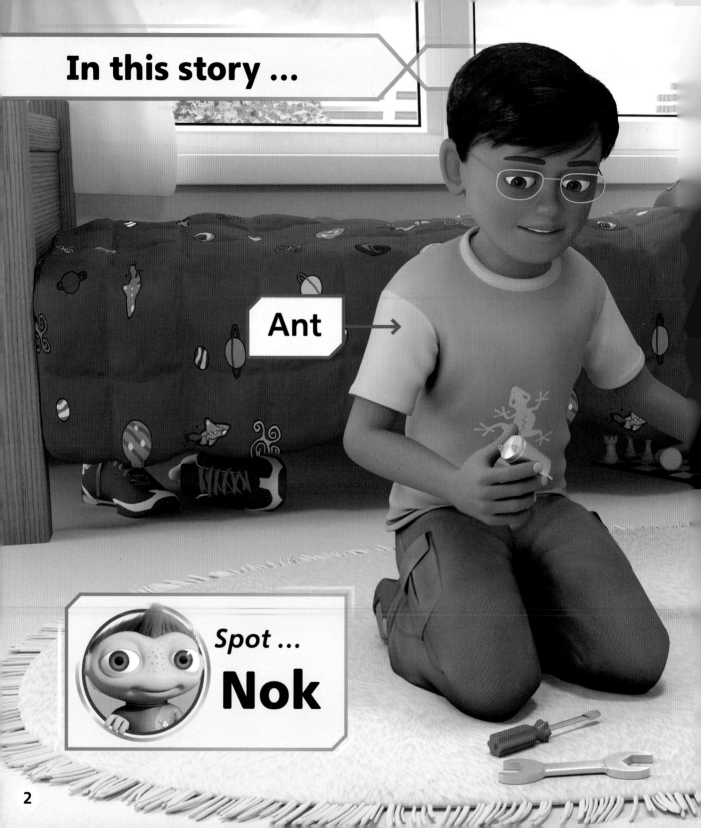

In this story ...

Ant

Spot ...
Nok

2

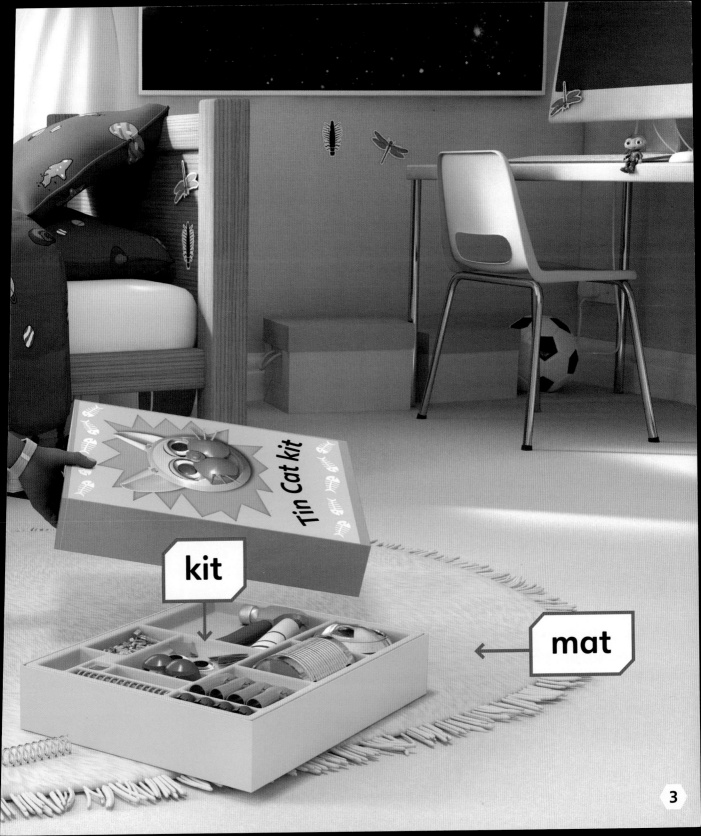

Tin Cat kit

kit

mat

3

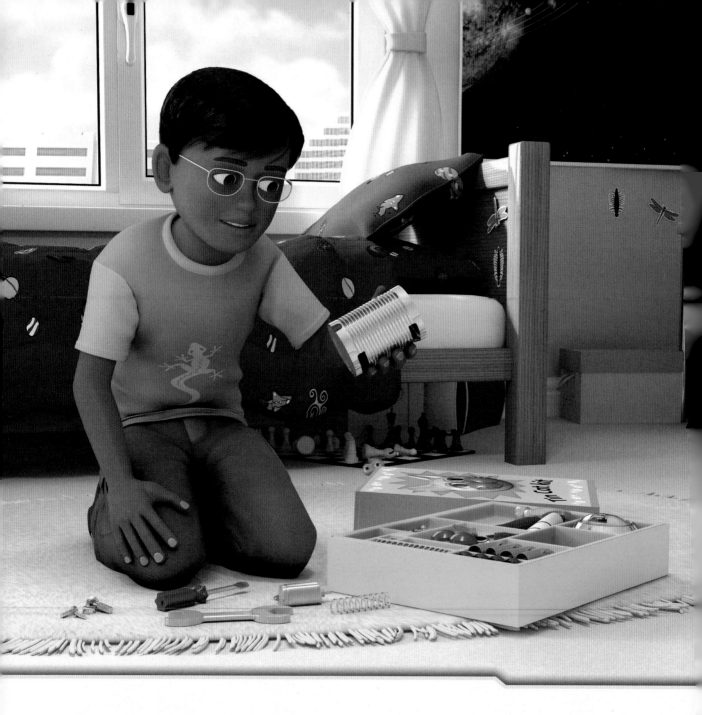

Ant got a tin.

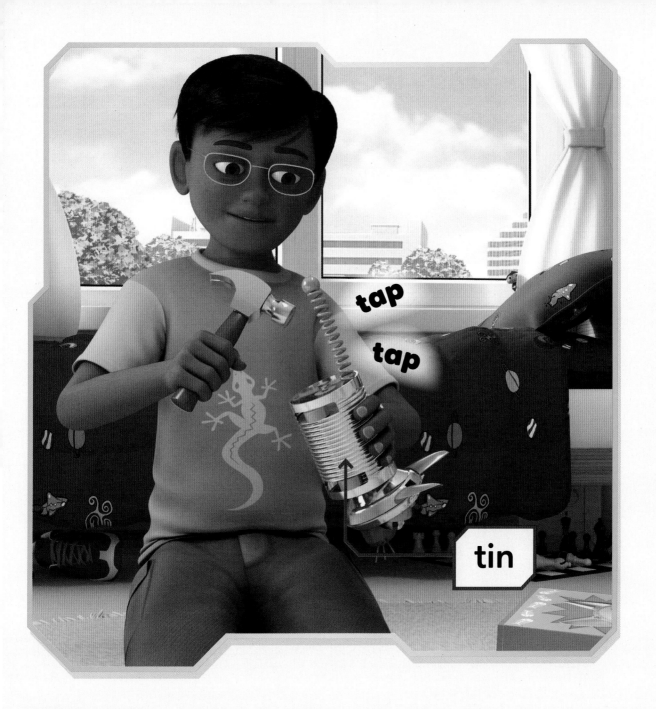

Ant taps on a tin.

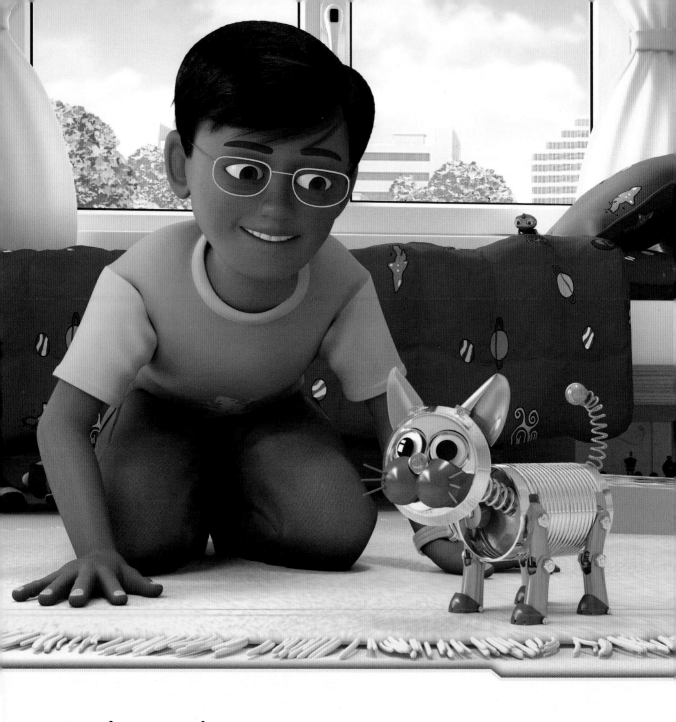

It is a tin cat!

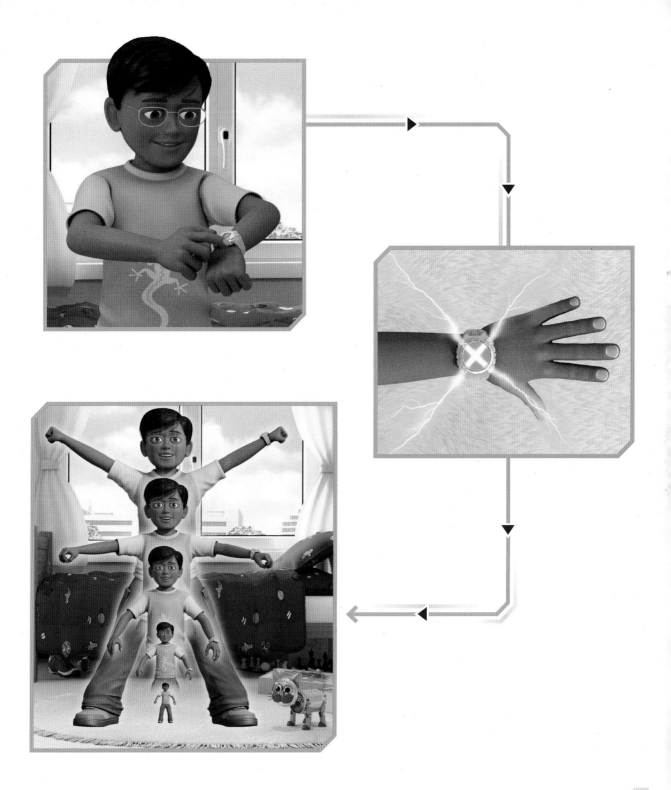

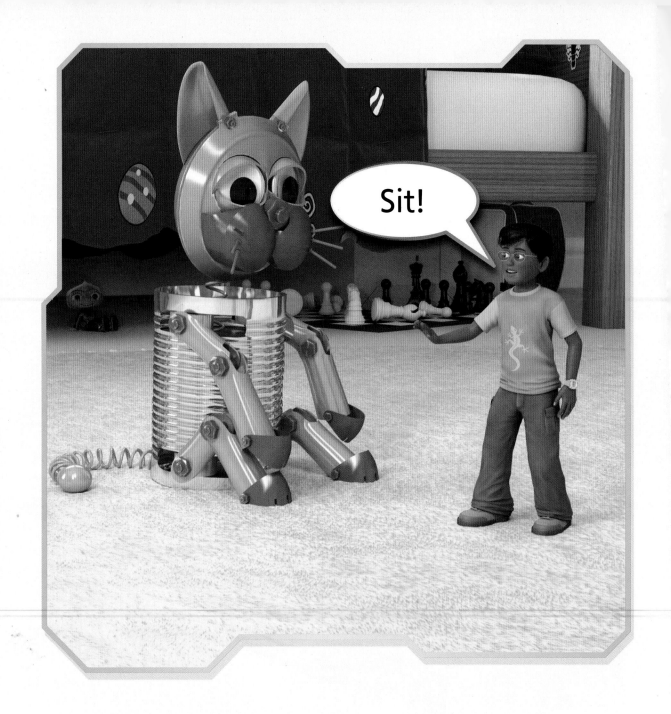

Tin Cat can sit.

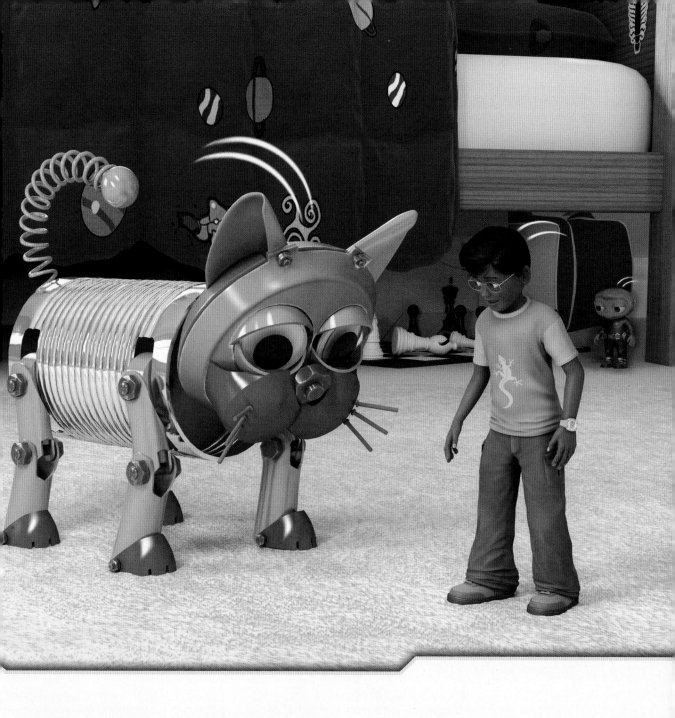

Tin Cat can nod.

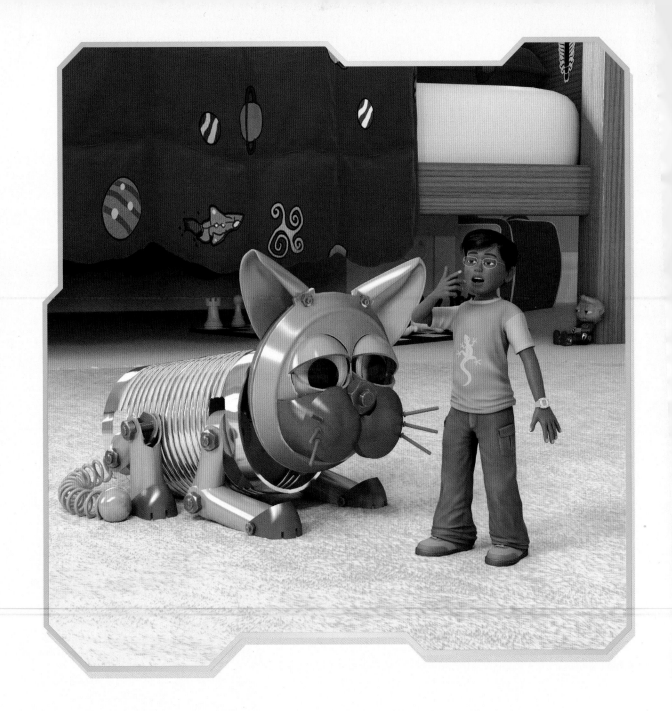

Tin Cat sags.

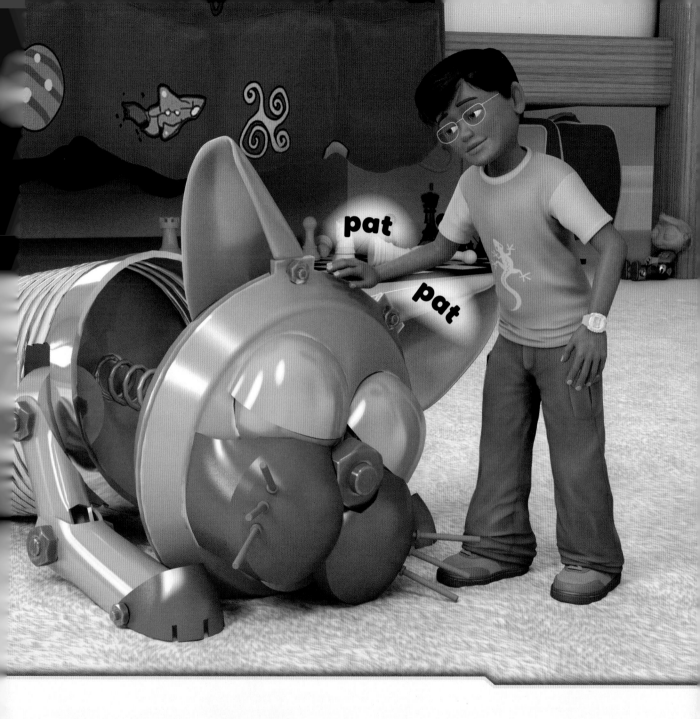

Tin Cat naps.

Retell the story

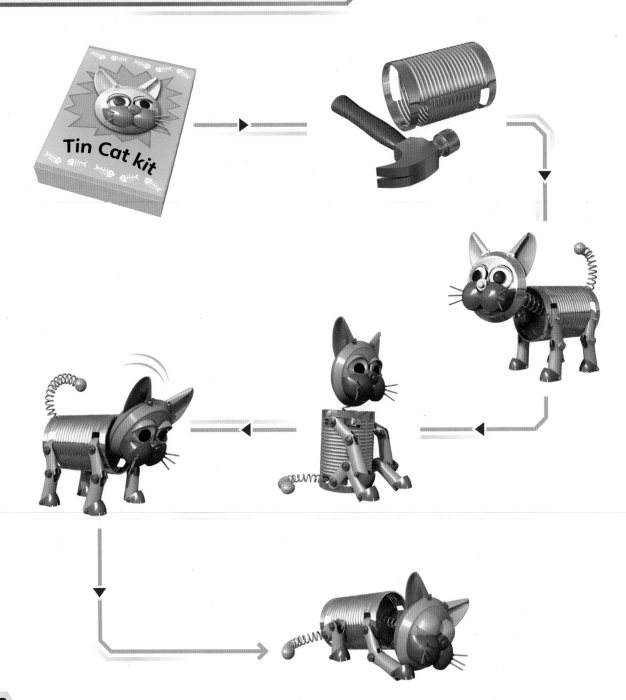